BRUSSELS SPROUTS & UNiCORNS

a book of rhymes

LIBRARY EDITION

BY ROBERT CHAPLiN *rca bfa*

© AD MMiX Robert Chaplin, all rights reserved.
Published in Canada by Robert Chaplin at libraryeditions.com
Library & Archives Canada Cataloguing in Publication
Chaplin, Robert, 1968- Brussels Sprouts & Unicorns / Robert Chaplin.
Poems. Rhymes & Happy Times. ISBN 978-1-894897-37-2
I. Title.
PS8555.H398138B78 2009   C811'.6   C2009-902127-7
PRINTED AT FRIESENS IN CANADA. FABRiQUE AU CANADA

WORD TO MY FAiRY GODMOTHER
WORD TO MY NORTH WiND GiRL
THiS BOOK iS DEDiCATED
TO THE CHiLDREN
ALEXANDER, IAN, JESSiE & KARLiE

TABLE OF CONTENTS

THE BRUSSELS SPROUT
testimonial *

SUNSHiNE

FLOWERS

BEES

THE TRUE STORY OF
THE THREE PiGS
Brick House Pig †

NiGHT FLYERS

THE TRUE LEGEND OF
GASSYJACK †

PiGS REViSiTED †

AMPHiBiANS

THE FAMiLY REUNiON
a mixed metaphor

TWO VARiATiONS ON
THE GREAT DANE
Hans Christian Andersen 1805–1875
The Emperor's New Clothes   The Princess & The Pea

PHYLUM MOLLUSCA
*The Octopus * Mussels*

THE OLD TESTAMENT
TRUTH ABOUT BAKiNG †

HiGH LEVEL
MATHEMATiCS
My Lemma † Arctic Notation in the Key of Pi †

THE VALUE OF GOLD
& PRiCE OF SKY †

DODO BiRDS & DiNOSAURS
*The Last Dodo * *
The Old Testament Truth about Dinosaurs †

THE WORLD'S SHORTEST FAiRY TALE †

THE END

CANADiAN FACTS
Oath Regarding the Existence of
Unicorns
Other Facts   The Beaver

* The Brussels Sprout was first carved as an objet d'art in hematite, then published as a dimensional illustration in bronze and in sterling. 'The Brussels Sprout Testimonial' isbn-1-894897-09-9 is the prize given to the celebrated recipient of the annual cookbook award at Barbara-Jo's Books to Cooks. The octopus rhyme was originally composed on a sculpture in magnetic basalt, carved by my hand, using diamonds and water. 'The Last Dodo' isbn-1-894897-16-1 was first published as a brooch in sterling. † These rhymes were originally produced as hand drawn manuscripts and sold in a series of drawing exhibitions over a five year period, in Vancouver BC Canada, at the beginning of the 21st Century.

SiNG & SHOUT
& DANCE ABOUT
THERE'S MAGIC iN
THE BRUSSELS SPROUT
BOiLED UP &
SERVED iN BUTTER
BAKED iN TO A PiE
I LOVE TO EAT
THE BRUSSELS SPROUT
TO GO WiTHOUT
WOULD MAKE ME CRY

HAVE FAiTH &
NEVER EVER DOUBT
THERE'S MAGIC iN
THE BRUSSELS SPROUT
iN CHEESE SAUCE
OR iN MiNESTRONE
I WiLL STAND & TESTiFY
I LOVE TO EAT
THE BRUSSELS SPROUT
TO GO WiTHOUT
I'D RATHER DiE!

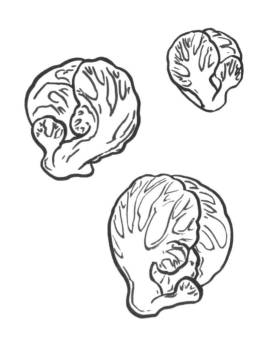

SUNSHiNE
MAKES ME FEEL FiNE
EASES MY MiND
HELPS ME UNWiND
SUNSHiNE
RELiEVES ALL MY PAiN
BETTER THAN RAiN
THANKS AGAiN
SUNSHiNE
FLOWERS
WE ARE ALL CiTY
AND ALL SEASON
iN CHERRY BLOSSOM
TiME
RHYME
WE BLOOM iN
WiNDOW BOXES
FLOWER POTS AND
FLOWER BEDS
THESE GARDENS
OUR HOME
THiS KiNGDOM RULED
BY DiViNE RiGHT AND
WORD
FLOWER
POWER

SNEEZY BEES SNEEZE
& SMOKEY BEES WHEEZE
HUNGRY BEES EAT PEAS
& DiRTY BEES HAVE FLEAS
BUSY BEES POLLiNATE
THE FLOWERS
& THE TREES
LOVING BEES PROPOSE UPON THEIR KNEES
POLiTE BEES SAY
PLEASE
& THANKYOU

ONCE UPON A TiME
AT A TiME WHEN
LiVESTOCK HAD PROPERTY
RiGHTS THERE LIVED
THREE PiGS
EACH OWNED LAND
AND BUiLT HOUSES
THE STUPiDEST PiG
BUILT A STRAW HOUSE
WHiCH BLEW DOWN WiTH
THE FiRST BiG STORM
THE iNSURANCE ADJUSTOR
JUST SHRUGGED
AND CUT THE
STRAW HOUSE PiG
A NiCE FAT CHEQUE. WHEN THE
STiCK HOUSE PiG
HEARD ABOUT THE iNSURANCE
HE HAD AN ACCiDENTAL FiRE
THEN THE TWO
HOMELESS PiGS
MOVED iN WiTH THE
BRiCK HOUSE PiG
THE MORTGAGE
GOT PAiD REAL FAST
THE MORAL OF THE STORY iS
iNSURANCE
HELPS TO EASE THE PAiN OF LOSS
BRiCK HOUSE

BATS AND OWLS FLY BY NiGHT BATS BY SOUND AND OWLS BY SiGHT

* The owl's eyes have evolved with excellent, long range, night vision. However, the owl has almost no sense of smell. The great horned owl (*Bubo virginianus*) willingly DiNES ON SKUNK * The sub order of bats known as *Microchiroptera* hunt by echolocation, meaning that these bats make high frequency noises and use their ears to track the sound bouncing back. These bats can differentiate between the sounds which bounce back and in this way LOCATE THEiR PREY

THE TRUE LEGEND OF GASSY JACK

JOHN DEiGHTON CAME FROM
ENGLAND AND WAS KNOWN AS

GASSY JACK

A MONiKER CONSiSTENT
WITH HIS CONSTANT

YAK YAK YAK

HiSTORiANS iNSiST THAT GASSY JACK
WAS A TALKATiVE SOUL
BUT THE SiMPLE TRUTH iS
HE HAD A WiNDY BOTTOM HOLE
JACK LiKED A GOOD FART
SO HE DiSTiLLED BEANS
AND MADE A HUNDRED PROOF JUiCE
THAT BLEW A HOLE iN HiS JEANS
THEN HE BUiLT A SALOON
WHERE HE SOLD HiS GASSY BREW

TO THE RESiDENTS OF GASTOWN
AND THEY ALL FARTED TOO
JACK MADE A LOT OF MONEY
FROM THiS GASEOUS DiSTiLLATiON
AND DiSTRiBUTED HiS BEVERAGE
TO FOLK FROM EVERY NATiON
THE BEANY DRiNK WAS PATENTED
AND MADE FANTASTiC CLAiMS
OF MEDiCATiON
GOOD FOR PiLES AND ALGEBRA
AND GREAT FOR CONSTiPATiON
JACK DRANK THE BEAN GROG EVERY DAY
TO CURE ALL OF HiS iLLS
HE SAiD THAT iT WAS BETTER THAN

THERAPY OR PiLLS

BY AND BY JACK'S DAiLY DOSE
DiD CAUSE iN HiM
A CONDiTiON OF THE HEART
BUT HE DiED BACK iN THE OUTHOUSE
WHEN HE BLEW HiS CHEEKS APART

THiS LiTTLE
PiGGY
MADE BACON

& THiS LiTTLE
PiGGY
MADE HAM

THiS LiTTLE
PiGGY
MADE PORK CHOPS

THiS LiTTLE
PiGGY MADE
SPAM

SALAMANDERS
NEWTS & TOADS & FROGS
MOSTLY COME FROM
POLLYWOGS

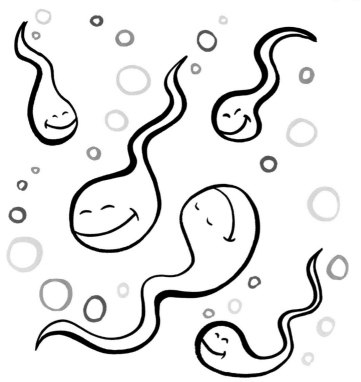

* The pollywog, aka tadpole is the fully aquatic larval stage in the amphibian life cycle The pollywog swims in the water and breathes with gills. During the metamorphosis to adulthood, lungs develop around the same time as legs. At this point the adult toad, frog, salamander or newt is no longer a pollywog and is prepared to spend at least some time on land.

WE HAD A FAMILY REUNiON
AND EVERYBODY CAME
UNCLE BEN & BETTY CROCKER
AUNT JEMiMA & THE QUAKER
MR CHRiSTiE & MRS BUTTERWORTH
THE BLUE NUN & THE RED MAN
THE GREEN GiANT & POCAHONTAS
FROM THE LAND O'LAKES
THE PiLLSBURY DOUGHBOY & THE ROBERTSON GOLLYWOG
COUNT CHOCULA & FRANKENBERRY
CHARLiE THE TUNA & CAPTAiN BiRDSEYE
THE CAMPBELL'S SOUP KiDS & THE GERBER BABY
& THE COUSiNS SNAP, CRACKLE, & POP
YOU ARE WHAT YOU EAT.
CAN'T PiCK YOUR RELATiVES

TWO VARiATiONS ON THE GREAT DANE

Hans Christian Andersen 1805–1875

THE EMPEROR MAKES ORDER BY IMPERiAL DECREE THAT HiS EXCELLENCY WiLL HAVE A PARADE TO HONOUR AND CELEBRATE THE VERY LATEST iN HAUTE COUTURE

THE EMPEROR WALKED PROUDLY DOWN THE STREET AS NAKED AS A JAY

CONViNCED THAT HiS NEW CLOTHES DiSPLAYED THE HiGHEST FASHiON OF THE DAY

A KiD SAiD TO THE CROWD, "EXCUSE ME EVERYONE, I DON'T MEAN TO BE RUDE BUT HAS ANYBODY TOLD THAT MAN HE iS COMPLETELY NUDE? HE iS AS RUSTiC AS A BRUTE, HE'S STROLLiNG iN HiS BiRTHDAY SUiT!"

THE CROWD, ALL STUPiD, SHOUTED, "SHUT-UP KiD THOSE ARE THE FiNEST CLOTHES HE CHOSE SO DON'T BE HOLDiNG UP YOUR NOSE FOR NEVER HAVE WE EVER SEEN SUCH FANTASTiC CLOTHES AS THOSE"

iF THERE'S A MORAL TO THiS TALE iT'S SiMPLY TO BE BOLD DESPiTE THE FACT MOST FOLKS BELiEVE EXACTLY WHAT THEY'RE TOLD

Said the Princess to the Pea

WHY iS iT THAT YOU PESTER ME?

THE BEDDiNG'S PiLED UP

TO THE CEiLiNG

YET I CANNOT

HELP THiS FEELiNG

OH SO WiCKED, NOT QUiTE RiGHT

WHY MUST

YOU KEEP

ME UP ALL

NiGHT?

Said the Pea unto the Princess

DARLiNG PRiNCESS

SO APPEALiNG

MATTRESSES UP TO THE CEiLiNG

iT iS YOU I WON'T STOP FEELiNG

LOVELiNESS, THiS TREAT DELiGHT

I MiGHT KEEP YOU

UP ALL NiGHT

Said the Princess to the Pea

STOP iT YOU MUST LET ME BE

iNSOMNiA HAS

GOT ME REELiNG

SHEETS AND BLANKETS TO THE CEiLiNG

iT'S TOO HOT, THE MOON'S TOO BRiGHT

WHY MUST

YOU KEEP

ME UP ALL

NiGHT?

Said the Pea unto the Princess

I WONT EVER STOP THiS FEELiNG

QUiLTS AND PiLLOWS

TO THE CEiLiNG

THiS iNTENTiON I'M REVEALiNG

I WiLL GiVE YOU NO RESPiTE

I'M GOiNG TO KEEP YOU

UP ALL NiGHT

Said the Princess to the Pea

WHY iS iT THAT YOU TORTURE ME?

CRUMPLED DUVETS TO THE CEiLiNG

STOP iT NOW. PLEASE STOP THiS FEELiNG

THiS MUST END!

OH PLEASE DON'T. STOP

I THiNK

MY HEAD

iS GOiNG

TO POP

Said the Pea unto the Princess

COME NOW PRiNCESS

STOP YOUR SQUEALiNG

I'M REPEALiNG

ALL THiS FEELiNG

REPOSE. SWEET DREAMS

SLEEP TiGHT STAR BRiGHT

I'LL KEEP YOU UP

TOMORROW NiGHT

THE OCTOPUS HAS

X

PHYLUM MOLLUSCA THiS GROUP OF ANiMALS iS VERY DiVERSE AND iNCLUDES ALMOST ONE HUNDRED THOUSAND EXTANT SPECiES APPROXiMATELY ONE QUARTER OF ALL MARINE LiFE BELONGS TO PHYLUM MOLLUSCA iNCLUDiNG OCTOPi SQUiDS, CLAMS, SLUGS SNAiLS, AND MUSSELS TiCKLES

AND LiVES BENEATH THE OCEAN THE OCTOPUS HAS VIII LOVELY LEGS TO AiD iN LOCOMOTiON

I LiKE NOTHiNG BETTER THAN
A MESS O' STEAMED MUSSELS
ALL JUiCY iN THE BROTH
iN THEiR STEAMY LiTTLE SHELLS
LiKE PRETTY MAiDS ALL iN A ROW
PiLED DEEPLY iN A BOWL
HAPPY LiTTLE BiVALVES
I CAN SLURP 'EM DOWN WHOLE
THEY ALL OPEN TO CONSUMPTiON
& WHEN THEY HAVE ALL BEEN ATE
I STACK THEiR USED UP SHELLS
UPON MY LiTTLE
SiDE PLATE

OLD TESTAMENT TRUTH ABOUT BAKiNG

EVE LiKED TO EAT THE FRUiT AND SHE LiKED TO MiND THE SNAKE

SHE GOTTA LOTTA KNOWLEDGE
THiNK SHE EVER LEARNED TO BAKE?

AN APPLE PiE FOR ADAM?
RHUBARB CRUMBLE FOR THE LORD?
A FRUiT FLAN FOR THE FLYiNG MAN
THE ANGRY ONE, WiTH FLAMiNG SWORD

NOW I'M NOT PRONE TO BLASPHEMY
OR FITS OF iDLE SPECULATiON
BUT IT iS MY HYPOTHESiS
MY THEORY, AND PET POSTULATiON

THAT
iF THAT
SWEET
WOMAN
LEARNED
TO BAKE
A CAKE
A CRUMBLE
OR A PiE
WE MiGHT LiVE
iN EDEN STiLL
NAKED
UNDER GOD'S
BLUE
SKY

HiGH LEVEL MATHEMATiCS

$$\frac{1+\sqrt{5}}{2} \quad :) \quad \pi$$

THE GOLDEN SECTiON iS SWEETER THAN Pi

FOR THE BENEFiT OF THE iLLNUMERATE A LEMMA iS A MATHEMATiCAL PREMiSE, A POiNT FROM WHiCH NEW MATHEMATiCAL FORMULAE MAY BE CREATED. THiS ONE USES THE SiDEWAYS HAPPY FACE TO DESCRiBE THE RELATiONSHiP BETWEEN TWO iRRATiONAL NUMBERS, WiTH RESPECT TO THEiR AESTHETiC VALUE. THE PROOF OF THiS STATEMENT iS EViDENT UPON EXAMiNATiON OF COMPOSiTiON iN FiNE ART. THE GOLDEN SECTiON CAN BE USED TO GENERATE A SPiRAL AND THROUGHOUT HiSTORY THE MOST ACCOMPLiSHED ARTiSTS HAVE USED THE GOLDEN SECTiON TO CREATE PLEASiNG COMPOSiTiONS. THE GOLDEN SECTiON iS ALSO KNOWN AS THE GOLDEN MEAN, THE GOLDEN RATiO, DiViNE PROPORTiON, AND PHi. ITS HARMONY CAN BE SEEN iN ART AND NATURE, iN CATHEDRALS AND SEASHELLS.

AN ESKiMO π

iS AN iRRATiONAL INUiT DESSERT

THE VALUE OF GOLD & PRiCE OF SKY

GENUiNE SOME FOLKS ARE SELLiNG LAND
NiNETY AND SOME FOLKS ARE SELLiNG WATER
NiNE I AM SELLiNG SKY
POiNT YOU GET A GALLON FOR A QUARTER
NiNE I'M SELLiNG iT SO CHEAP JUST BECAUSE I'M FEELiNG FiNE
FiNE YOU GET A FiVE GALLON BUCKET FOR A DOLLAR SiXTY-NiNE
SHiNE iF YOU WANT A VOLUME DiSCOUNT
I HAVE A SWEET SWEET DEAL FOR YOU
IS A HUNDRED GALLON TANK, WiTH WEEKLY FiLLUP
FOR ONE HUNDRED NiNETY-TWO
iF iNVESTiNG iN THE MARKET'S
SOMETHiNG YOU WOULD LiKE TO TRY
FOR JUST TEN THOUSAND DOLLARS, THERE'S
POiNT 'THE BALANCED GOLDEN SUNSET FUND' FOR YOU TO BUY
ONE AND FOR ONE HUNDRED THOUSAND, YOU CAN GET
BLUE CHiP FOR TO SELL! 'CAUSE I DON'T LiE
PERCENT AND YOU CAN REST YOUR MiND AND SAFELY
PERCEPTiON PUT YOUR MiLLiON iNTO FUTURES iN THE SKY

THE LAST DODO

ALTHOUGH THE DATE
THE LAST DODO
DiED iS UNKNOWN
THE SPECiES WAS EXTiNCT
BY THE LATE 1600s
THE LAST DODO
SPECIMEN, HOWEVER, WAS
CONSiGNED TO FLAMES
iN iGNORANCE
AT THE ASHMOLEAN
MUSEUM, OXFORD

1755

WAS iT SHABBY AND ROTTEN? WAS iT CREEPY AND RUDE?
WAS THE CURATOR JUST iN A HOUSE CLEANiNG MOOD?
WAS iT BAD TAXiDERMY? WAS iT DUSTY AND OLD?
WAS iT FLEA BiTTEN, MANGY, OR GROWiNG SOME MOLD?
WAS iT REALLY SUBVERSiVE? WAS iT SMELLY AND PUTRiD?
WAS iT AESTHETiCALLY WEAK? WERE THE TRUSTEES ALL STUPiD?
ALL QUESTiONS HAVE ANSWERS. BUT WE'LL LiKELY GET SPURNED
iF AT OXFORD WE ASK WHY THE DODO GOT BURNED

THE LIONS
ATE THE
UNICORN*
AT NIGHT
WHEN IT WAS DARK

& THERE
NEVER WAS A
DINOSAUR
ON BOARD OF
NOAH'S ARK
THERE WERE
GRIZZLY BEARS
& WORKING
BEAVERS*
BULL MOOSE
& CHICKADEES
GIRAFFES
& MOUNTAIN GOATS
& BIGHORN SHEEP
& HONEYBEES
ELEPHANTS
& CATS & BIRDS
& LITTLE DOGS
(WHO LIKE TO BARK)
BUT THERE
NEVER WAS A
DINOSAUR
ON BOARD OF
NOAH'S ARK
AMEN

ONCE
UPON
A TiME
EVERYONE
LiVED
HAPPiLY
EVER
AFTER

THE END

fin

CANADiAN FACTS

THE BEAVER (*castor canadensis*)

THE BEAVER iS THE HARDEST WORKING ANiMAL iN CANADA. BEAVERS CHOP DOWN TREES, AND USE STiCKS AND MUD, TO DAM CREEKS AND MAKE PONDS TO SWiM iN. BEAVERS ALSO BUiLD LODGES FROM STiCKS AND MUD. THE BEAVER LODGE PROViDES SHELTER AND PROTECTION FROM PREDATORS AND CONSTiTUTES THE BEAVER'S HOME. BEAVERS ARE RODENTS, MEANiNG THEY HAVE A PAiR OF BUCK TEETH INCiSORS THAT CONTiNUE TO GROW. THE BEAVER'S TEETH ARE KEPT SHORT BY GNAWING, WHiCH iN THE BEAVER'S CASE, MEANS CHEWiNG ON WOOD TO BUiLD DAMS AND LODGES.

THE BEAVER'S FAVORiTE FOOD iS WATERLiLiES. BEAVERS HAVE WEBBED FEET, WHiCH HELP THE BEAVER TO SWiM AND CATCH WATERLiLiES. THE BEAVER ALSO HAS A BROAD, SCALY, FLAT TAiL. WHEN THE BEAVER iS FRiGHTENED OR STARTLED iT MAKES A LOUD SLAPPiNG SOUND ON THE WATER BY USING iTS TAiL. THESE LOUD SOUNDS WARN OTHER BEAVERS AND FOREST CREATURES OF DANGER.

THE NORTH AMERiCAN GiANT

BEAVER (*castoroides ohioensis*) WAS ONE OF THE LARGEST RODENTS TO EVER WALK THE EARTH. GiANT BEAVERS WERE ABOUT THE SAME SiZE AS MODERN BLACK BEARS, AND BECAME EXTiNCT ABOUT 13,000 YEARS AGO. MODERN BEAVERS ARE MUCH SMALLER AND MAKE BETTER PETS, HATS, AND FRiENDS.

Oath regarding the existence of unicorns

THE MONARCHY **OF CANADA** FAITHFULLY ACKNOWLEDGES **THE UNICORN** *&* PROTECTS ITS EXISTENCE BY PROVIDING SAFE UNICORN HABITAT ON THE ROYAL CANADIAN **COAT OF ARMS**

other facts

AVRiL PHAEDRA DOUGLAS CAMPBELL *aka* KIM CAMPBELL, BORN 1947 BECAME THE FIRST WOMAN PRIME MINISTER OF CANADA IN 1993 STEVE FONYO, BORN 1965 WAS THE FIRST ONE LEGGED MAN TO SUCCESSFULLY RUN ACROSS CANADA ROBERT HOMME *aka* THE FRIENDLY GIANT, BORN 1919 WAS A REKNOWNED THESPIAN *&* STOOD 5 FEET 6 INCHES TALL ARCHIBALD STANSFELD BELANEY *aka* GREY OWL, BORN 1888 WAS A CELEBRATED WILDLIFE CONSERVATIONIST *&* KEPT PET BEAVERS IN HIS HOUSE.